© 1984 by Faber Music Ltd
First published in 1984 by Faber Music Ltd
3 Queen Square London WC1N 3AU
Music drawn by Sheila Stanton
Photograph by Ben Johnson
Cover design by Shirley Tucker
Printed in England
All rights reserved

Explanation of Signs : Zeichenerklärung

Barré: The horizontal line shows the duration of the *barré*. The vertical line indicates how many of the strings should be covered. The Roman numeral indicates the fret.

Barré: Die waagrechte Linie zeigt die Dauer des Barrégriffs an. Die senkrechte Linie gibt an, wieviele Saiten erfasst werden müssen. Die römische Ziffer bezeichnet den Bund.

Harmonics are indicated at their actual pitch with a diamond note-head.

Die Obertöne sind an der Stelle ihrer tatsächlichen Tonhöhe durch eine Raute bezeichnet.

The left hand finger should remain on the string, touching it very lightly when shifting to the next note. The notes in between should not sound.

Der Finger der linken Hand sollte auf der Saite bleiben und sie sehr leicht berühren, wenn er auf die nächste Note überwechselt. Die dazwischenliegenden Noten sollten nicht anklingen.

First Repertoire for Solo Guitar

BOOK 1

Erstes Repertoire für Sologitarre

BAND 1

edited by

SIMON WYNBERG

Faber Music Limited

London

Bärenreiter-Verlag, Kassel : Boosey & Hawkes (Australia) Pty. Ltd., Sydney
Boosey & Hawkes (Canada) Ltd., Willowdale : G. Schirmer Inc., New York

Preface

Guitar teachers have long complained about the dearth of a varied and musically stimulating diet for students in their first years of study; this book aims to provide an alternative to the usual old chestnuts and ubiquitous arrangements. All of the pieces are original guitar compositions, many of which have not been issued since their first appearance in the eighteenth and nineteenth centuries. Others, including works by José Ferrer, are presented here for the very first time.

The well-known problem of adapting Baroque guitar music for the modern instrument, with all the attendant difficulties of tuning and ornamentation, accounts for the nineteenth-century bias of the present collection. However, in an effort to provide a broader selection of works we have commissioned pieces from two contemporary composers, Nicholas Maw and Stanley Glasser, and these have expanded the technical and musical range of the book considerably.

In preparing this edition, I have used the earliest and most reliable sources. Only in the transcriptions of the Baroque works have a few minor changes been made. Most left hand and all right hand fingering is editorial (both are intentionally rather sparse at times, as students should be encouraged to add their own), and notation has been modernised where necessary. All editorial additions have been placed in square brackets, and notes on performance have been added after each piece. The compositions have been arranged in approximate order of difficulty.

I am particularly grateful to Robert Spencer, who allowed me to delve into his remarkable music collection, gave encouragement and made suggestions, and by whose kind permission much of the following is published.

SIMON WYNBERG

Einleitung

Lange Zeit haben Gitarrenlehrer das Fehlen einer abwechslungsreichen und musikalisch anregenden Kost für Schüler in den Anfangsjahren beklagt. Dieser Band will eine Alternative zu den üblichen "alten Kamellen" und überall zu findenden Arrangements bieten. Alle diese Stücke sind Originalkompositionen für die Gitarre, von denen viele seit ihrer Erstveröffentlichung im achtzehnten und neunzehnten Jahrhundert nicht mehr herausgegeben wurden. Andere wiederum, wie z.B. die Werke Jose Ferrers, erscheinen hier zum allerersten Mal.

Das wohlbekannte Problem der Bearbeitung von Gitarrenmusik des Barock für das moderne Instrument mit all den damit verbundenen Schwierigkeiten des Stimmens und der Ornamentierung, erklärt das Vorherrschen von Musik des neunzehnten Jahrhunderts in der vorliegenden Sammlung. Dennoch haben wir uns darum bemüht, eine größere Auswahl an Werken zu bieten, und zu diesem Zweck Stücke bei zwei zeitgenössischen Komponisten in Auftrag gegeben, Nicholas Maw und Stanley Glasser, wobei diese die technische und musikalische Spannweite des Bandes beträchtlich erweitert haben.

Bei der Vorbereitung dieser Ausgabe habe ich die frühesten und zuverlässigsten Quellen verwendet. Lediglich in den Transkriptionen der Barockstücke wurden einige geringfügige Änderungen vorgenommen. Der größte Teil des Fingersatzes für die linke Hand und der gesamte Fingersatz für die rechte Hand sind editorisch (beide sind manchmal absichtlich recht spärlich gehalten, da die Schüler dazu angeregt werden sollen, ihre eigenen Fingersätze hinzuzufügen), und die Notation wurde, wenn nötig, modernisiert. Alle editorischen Hinzufügungen wurden in eckige Klammern gesetzt, und das Spiel betreffende Anmerkungen nach jedem Stück beigefügt. Die Kompositionen wurden nach ungefähr fortschreitendem Schwierigkeitsgrad angeordnet.

Insbesondere bin ich Robert Spencer dankbar, der mir erlaubte, mich in seiner bemerkenswerten Notensammlung umzusehen, der ermutigte und Vorschläge machte, und mit dessen freundlicher Erlaubnis ein großer Teil der folgenden Stücke veröffentlicht wird.

SIMON WYNBERG
Deutsche Übersetzung: Dorothee Eberhardt

Contents : Inhalt

1. Etude

FERNANDO SOR
Op.60 No.3

[Moderato e molto legato]

2. Ejercicio

JOSE FERRER

Allegro moderato

3. Amusement

FELIX HORETZKY
Op.18 No.10

4. Un jour me demandoit Hortence

IGNAZ PLEYEL
arr. F. Chabran

4

5. Valtz

DIONISIO AGUADO
Op.10 No.19

[Andante]

poco rit.

6. Etude

FERNANDO SOR
Op.60 No.4

[Larghetto]

7. Etude

FERNANDO SOR
Op. 35 No. 2

Andantino

8. Allegro

MAURO GUILIANI
Op. 50 No. 1

Allegro

9. Valze

FERDINANDO CARULLI
Op.50 No.7

10. Allegretto & Allegro

PIERRE PORRO

11. Amusement

FELIX HORETZKY
Op.18 No.8

12. Amusement

FELIX HORETZKY
Op.18 No.9

[Andante]

13. Maestoso

MAURO GIULIANI
Op.51 No.1

Maestoso

14. *Allegro Moderato*

PIERRE PORRO

15. Etude

FERNANDO SOR
Op.60 No.13

[Larghetto]

[mf] [molto legato]

16. Galop

MATTEO CARCASSI
Op.39 No.1

[Allegro]

17. Pastoral

DIONISIO AGUADO
Op.10 No.17

18. Galop

MATTEO CARCASSI
Op.39 No.10

19. Menuet

SANTIAGO DE MURCIA

20. Andantino

MAURO GIULIANI
Op. 51 No. 10

21. Galop

MATTEO CARCASSI
Op.39 No.8

22. Gaillarde

GUILLAUME MORLAYE

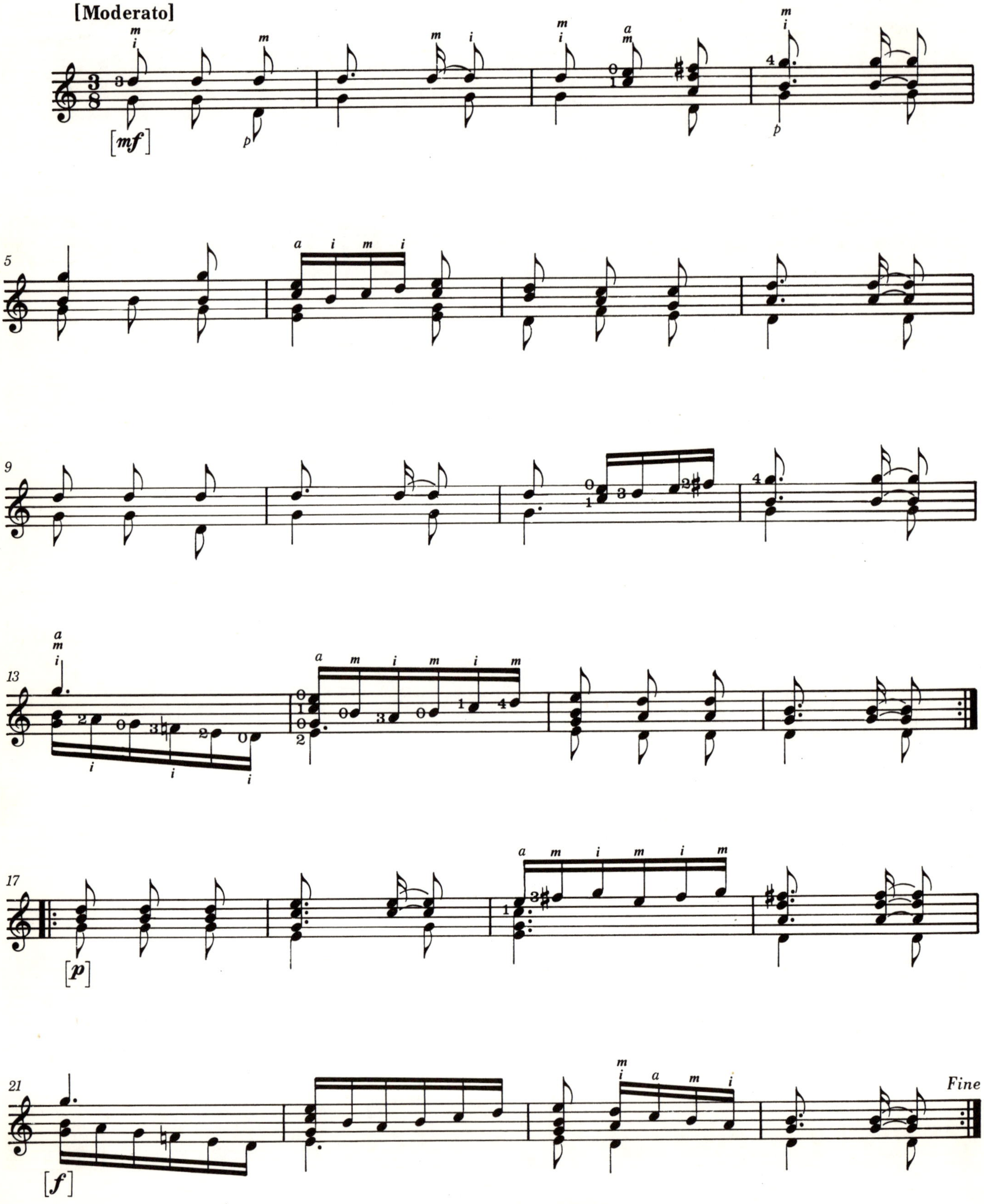

23. Bransle

GUILLAUME MORLAYE

24. Gavotte

ROBERT DE VISÉE

25. Sicilienne

FERDINANDO CARULLI
Op.34 No.2

26. Ejercicio

JOSE FERRER

27. La Dessine

SANTIAGO DE MURCIA

28. Ejercicio

JOSE FERRER

29. Buffons

GUILLAUME MORLAYE

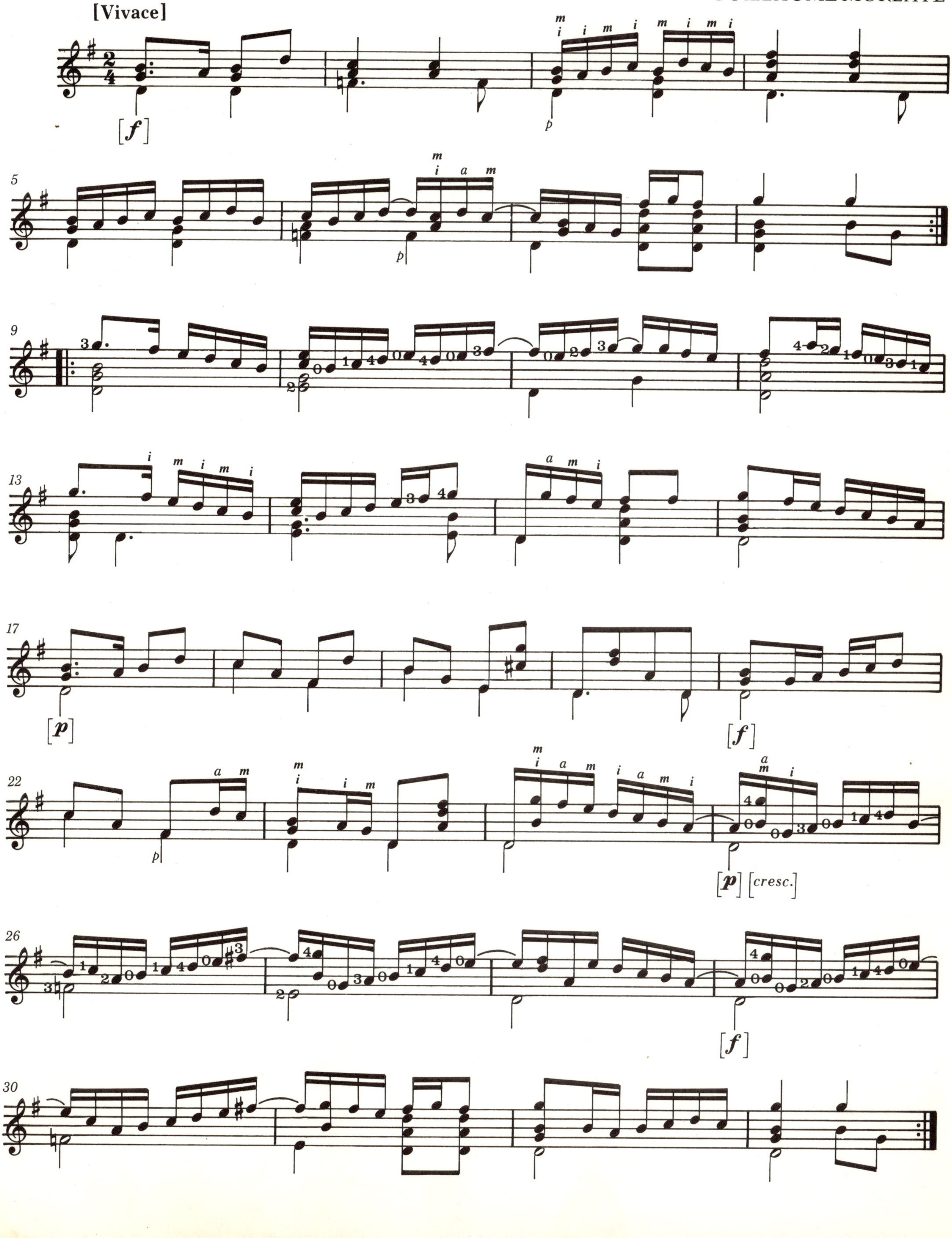

30. *Reflection*

NICHOLAS MAW

Andante melancolico

31. Song

NICHOLAS MAW

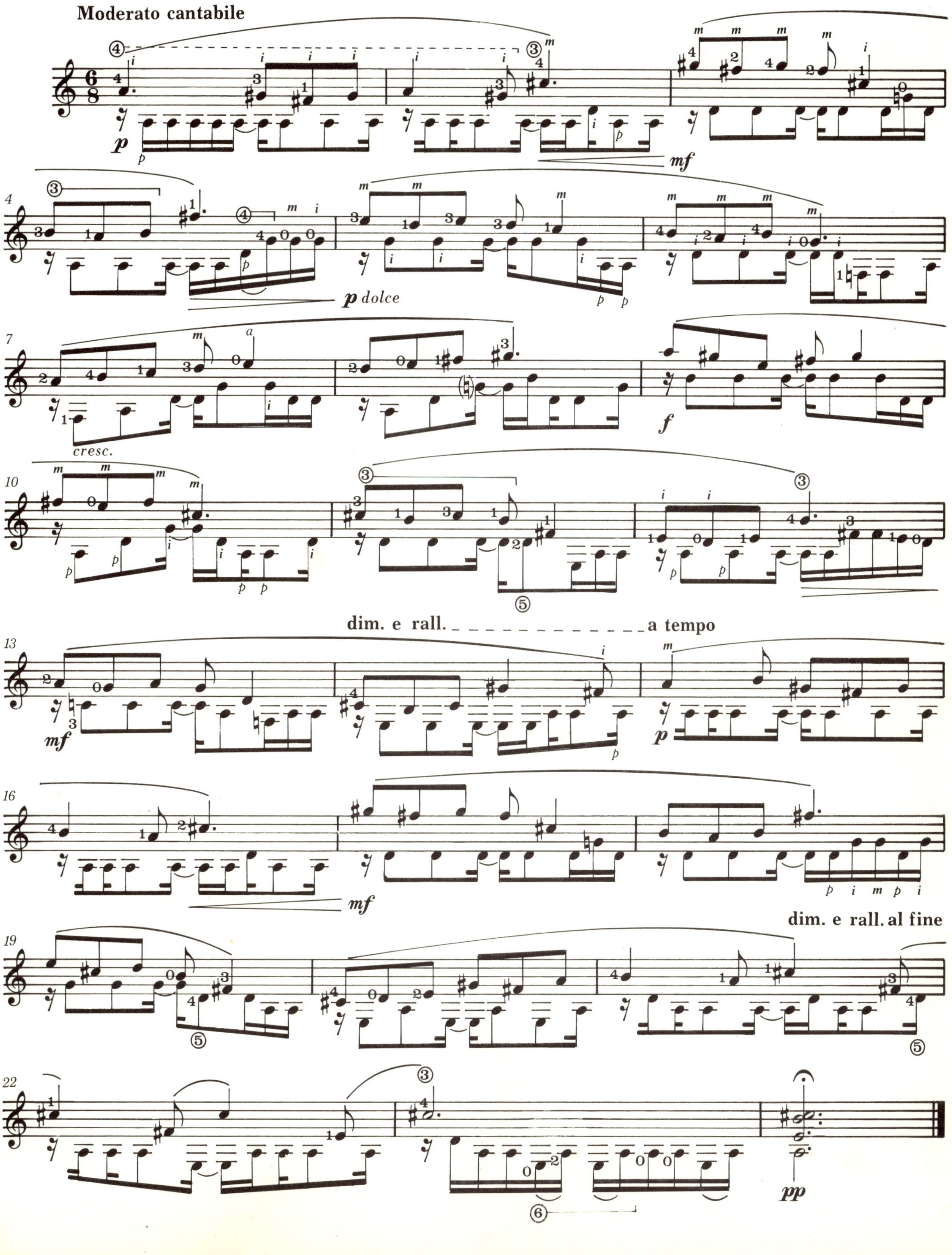

32. Obsesión

GUILLERMO FLORES MÉNDEZ

Largo: un poco rubato (♩ = 52)

poco più mosso (♩ = 72)

33. Miniatura

Allegro (♪ = 132)

GUILLERMO FLORES MÉNDEZ

24

34. Striding

STANLEY GLASSER

Semplice (♩ = c. 80)

35. Mlengana Rock

STANLEY GLASSER

Lento e tenebroso

ad lib.

A tempo, molto lento (♩. = c. 36)

come prima

36. Pig in a Rain Puddle

STANLEY GLASSER

37. Donkey Ride

STANLEY GLASSER

1 Fernando Sor was one of the most important composers for the guitar in the nineteenth century. This melody should be played very smoothly using a *tirando* stroke for the thumb.

2 From *6ª Coleccion de Ejercicios*. The accompaniment is best played very quietly, the bass more strongly. Avoid resting the thumb on the string before playing the note.

3 In this piece, both voices are equally important and neither bass nor treble should predominate. The small crossed note, called an *acciaccatura*, must be played on the beat with the G in the bass.

4 From *6 Favourite Songs and 6 Favourite Rondos*. This melody was intended for the English guitar, an instrument with wire strings tuned to a C major chord. The small note, called an *appoggiatura*, takes half the value of the one that follows. It should be played with a gentle push:

5 Dionisio Aguado was a friend and colleague of Fernando Sor. Unlike Sor, however, he used nails on his right hand. For this charming little waltz, maintain a steady three-in-a-bar rhythm, emphasising the first beat very slightly. The *acciaccaturas* must be played very quickly. Do not be reluctant to *throw* down the left hand fingers hard.

6 This C minor melody is a little more awkward than it seems. The musical sense may be made clearer if each phrase is sung a few times, as well as played. The first beat of the bar should not be over-emphasised; doing so will ruin the musical flow. The open notes, particularly the Gs, must not ring on longer than their actual duration.

7 This piece sounds most effective if the melody notes *do* ring over one another. Chords played on the bass strings should not sound muddy but be as well defined as those in the higher register.

8 While Sor and Aguado were Spanish, Mauro Giuliani was a brilliant Italian virtuoso who wrote a vast amount for the instrument. This work is one of the best-known of his easier pieces. It still sounds effective even at a moderate tempo – clarity is most important here. Every semi-quaver of the accompaniment pattern is equally important.

9 Ferdinando Carulli was born in Naples, but lived much of his life in Paris, the centre of the guitar world in the early nineteenth century. It is essential to hold the melody notes for their full duration and to avoid stressing the notes in the accompaniment which are played with the thumb.

10. From *Exercises* Op. 24. The French guitarist Pierre Porro wrote this piece for the guitar in use at the end of the eighteenth century; this instrument had paired strings, called courses, and no low E string. The first section should be played briskly and strongly.

11 The middle notes of the three and four part chords ought to be as clear as the outer parts. The full *barré* on the last line is rather difficult. The G may be omitted to avoid playing it. In the penultimate bar, the bass Gs should be held for a full crotchet.

12 All the bass notes should be held (and be heard to be held). The right hand fingering is supplied in full, but it is worth experimenting with other patterns. There are often many solutions to right hand fingering problems.

13 Do not be tempted to play this too quickly. *Maestoso* means 'with dignity' and implies a stately tempo. There should be no audible gaps between the notes. Those marked *sf* must be accented but not harshly.

14 From *Exercises* Op. 24. The significant word in the tempo indication is *Moderato*. If the opening is too fast, the semi-quavers will be unmanageable. In the opening section, ensure that the sound ceases for the rests. In the arpeggio passages, the bass notes should be played firmly.

15 In this piece, it may be helpful to think of the strings as being red hot; the right hand fingers can touch them, but only for a short time. The note is played as the finger comes into contact with the string; this will help to obtain a smooth, joined line. Once again, both parts must be clearly distinguishable.

16 The Galop was a quick, lively dance popular during the nineteenth century. The semi-quavers should not drag. Repeats can be played *piano*.

17 The mood of this *Pastoral* should be relaxed, with a gentle swinging motion. The ornament in bar 2 should be played quickly and on the beat. Do not be too concerned if it does not 'speak' immediately; it is not at all easy.

18 The quaver bass notes should be stopped with the right hand thumb immediately as they are played. They are not as effective if allowed to ring on. A strict two-in-the-bar should be maintained.

19 The Spaniard Santiago de Murcia published his *Resumen de Acompañar*, from which this *Menuet* is taken, for the five course guitar. As in most Baroque guitar music, there are many ornaments. It may be best to omit them at first, adding them once the piece is fluent. The ornamentation should not affect the grace or the rhythm of the melody.

20 The thumb should glide over the first two notes in the bass pattern. The accompaniment should be discreet throughout.

21 All the harmonics (diamond-headed notes) are natural, played by lightly touching the strings at the twelfth, or, in the case of the high D, the seventh fret. Set the tempo by the speed at which you can play the harmonics comfortably.

22 From *Le Second Livre* of 1553 (22v). Very little is known about the sixteenth century lutenist and guitarist Guillaume Morlaye, including the dates of his birth and death. The compositions for the four-course guitar, transcribed here from the original tablature, are the earliest in this collection. The four-course instrument had four pairs of strings tuned D G B E, like the top four strings of the modern guitar. This *Gaillarde* (or *Galliard*) a popular dance of the day, should be played with a sprightly and pointed rhythm.

23 From *Le Second Livre* of 1553 (24v). While the *Gaillarde* (no. 22) has Italian roots, the *Bransle* (or *Branle*) was originally a rustic French dance. It was also popular in England, where it was known as the *Brawl*. The semi-quavers should be practiced very slowly, with careful attention to the right hand fingering.

24 Robert de Visée's *Gavotte* is taken from a manuscript in the Bibliothéque Nationale in Paris (Res F. 844, p. 200) and dates from around the end of the seventeenth century. As in the piece by Santiago de Murcia, there are many ornaments and again it may be worthwhile, initially, to omit the ornamentation in order to develop a secure rhythm. It is most effective to use the index finger for strumming the strings top-to-bottom.

25 Play this with a steady, rocking rhythm, like a lullaby. The rests should be strictly observed and none added between chords! The last four bars can be played very softly, gradually fading away.

26 No. 9 of *Collecion 10ª de Ejercicios*. Jose Ferrer, a native of Barcelona, wrote a large number of exercises and studies, most of which appear never to have been published. This *Vals*, like so many of his compositions, evokes a strongly Spanish atmosphere. In the descending passage of bars 5-7, the top note of each group may be held until the beginning of the next bar. The bass notes in the second section should be played strongly, with an *apoyando* attack.

27 From *Resumen de Acompañar* of 1714 (p. 84). Play this simply, ensuring the clarity of both parts. Trills for music of this period generally begin on the note above the written one, indicated here by acciaccaturas.

28 No. 2 of *Collection 12ª de Ejercicios*. This lively piece should be played with charm and humour, making sure that the chords in bar three are played clearly and in time. The grace notes are most effectively played quickly and strongly, on the beat.

29 From *Le Premier Livre* of 1552 (23v). The runs in *Buffons* (Clowns) should be practiced slowly, with the minimum of finger movement in both hands; gradually bring them up to a quicker speed. When well-played, this makes an impressive and exuberant concert piece.

30 & 31 These two pieces have been specially composed for this collection by the English composer Nicholas Maw. In no. 30, the

time signature may seem a little strange at first, but it is often found in modern compositions. It should not pose any problems if counted carefully. The thumb arpeggios ought not to be played too aggressively. To play them slower, sweep the thumb down diagonally, starting on the bass E string at the soundhole and moving towards the bridge for the treble strings. In no. 31, the open basses have been cleverly used by the composer to make an interesting rhythmic accompaniment; this should not sound laboured or intrude on the melody.

32 & 33 Guillermo Flores Méndez is a contemporary Mexican composer who has written much music for the guitar. *Obsesión* is best played at a very slow and measured tempo; note the composer's metronome indication. The same speed must be maintained for the syncopated middle section, and the D♯ and E kept clear and regular. No.33, from *Cuatro Miniaturas*, is really a relaxed waltz.

34-37 Stanley Glasser has written this suite incorporating various African musical elements. In the last two bars of *Striding*, the side of the thumb can be used to bang on the bridge. This effect is known as *tamburo*. In the last bar, the second finger should slide up the neck to the A, without being lifted off the fingerboard, in a rather swift motion. Notice in *Mlengana Rock* that the commas (brief pauses, and

not as long as ⌢) are placed in between the musical statements, making this movement much less difficult than would otherwise be the case. Note also the sudden dynamic changes, especially at the end. These pieces are quite different in their sound-world from anything else in this collection. Each musical sentence ought to be treated as a little piece in its own right; this will assist in appreciating the composition as a whole.

Pig in a Rain Puddle attempts to illustrate, in musical terms, a pig struggling to free itself. The boxes and arrows might seem very curious at first; their purpose is to provide the player with the opportunity of deciding on the end result of the piece: start with 1 and follow the arrows; repeat in a different order but end with 5 . The chance element that the player's choice introduces is known as *aleatoricism*. The downward slide (glissando) in box 3 is the same as that found in *Striding*. The signs + and ♯ mean one quarter-tone sharp and three-quarters of a tone sharp respectively. (Raise by bending the string.)

The accents in *Donkey Ride* are rather important; the > sign demands a sharper attack than the − sign, which is more of a weighted accent. There is a donkey bray hidden in the piece.

---

1 Fernando Sor war einer der wichtigsten Komponisten von Gitarrenmusik des neunzehnten Jahrhunderts. Diese Melodie sollte sehr legato, mit einem *Tirando*-Anschlag für den Daumen gespielt werden.

2 Aus *6ª Coleccion de Ejercicios*. Die Begleitung wird am besten sehr leise gespielt, die Baßstimme stärker angeschlagen. Vermeide es, vor dem Spielen der Note den Daumen auf der Saite ruhen zu lassen.

3 In diesem Stück sind beide Stimmen von gleicher Bedeutung, d.h. weder Baß- noch Oberstimme sollten dominieren. Die kleine durchstrichene Note heißt *Vorschlag* und muß, mit dem G im Baß, auf dem Taktschlag gespielt werden.

4 Aus *6 Favourite Songs and 6 Favourite Rondos*. Diese Melodie war für die englische Gitarre gedacht, ein Instrument mit Drahtsaiten, die zu einem C-Akkord gestimmt waren. Die kleine Note heißt *langer Vorschlag* (oder *Appoggiatura*) und erhält die Hälfte des Wertes der folgenden Note. Sie sollte mit einem leichten Akzent gespielt werden:

5 Dionisio Aguado war ein Freund und Kollege Fernando Sors. Anders als Sor jedoch spielte er mit Nägeln an der rechten Hand. Halte für diesen reizenden kleinen Walzer einen gleichmäßigen Rhythmus mit drei Schlägen pro Takt ein, und betone dabei sehr leicht den ersten Taktschlag. Die *Vorschläge* müssen sehr schnell gespielt werden. Zögere nicht, mit den Fingern der linken Hand hart aufzugreifen.

6 Diese Melodie in c-moll ist ein wenig schwieriger als sie zu sein scheint. Der musikalische Sinn kann dadurch verdeutlicht werden, daß jede Phrase ein paarmal gesungen und gespielt wird. Der erste Schlag des Taktes sollte nicht überbetont werden, da dies den musikalischen Fluß zerstört. Die offenen Noten, vor allem die Gs, dürfen nicht länger klingen als vorgeschrieben ist.

7 Dieses Stück klingt am wirkungsvollsten, wenn die Noten der Melodie ineinander klingen. Die Akkorde auf den Baßsaiten sollten nicht verschwommen, sondern genauso klar klingen wie die der oberen Register.

8 Während Sor und Aguado aus Spanien kamen, war Mauro Giuliani ein brillanter italienischer Virtuose, der eine große Anzahl von Stücken für das Instrument schrieb. Dieses Werk ist eines der bekanntesten seiner leichteren Stücke. Es klingt sogar in gemäßigtem Tempo noch eindrucksvoll – Klarheit ist hier überaus wichtig. Jedes Sechzehntel des Begleitmotivs ist gleichermaßen wichtig.

9 Ferdinando Carulli wurde in Neapel geboren, lebte jedoch für

einen großen Teil seines Lebens in Paris, das zu Anfang des neunzehnten Jahrhunderts das Zentrum des Gitarrenspiels war. In diesem Stück ist es äußerst wichtig, daß die Noten der Melodie in ihrer ganzen Länge ausgehalten, und die Noten der Begleitung, die mit dem Daumen gespielt werden, nicht betont werden.

10 Aus *Exercices* Op.24. Der französische Gitarrist Pierre Porro schrieb dieses Stück für die am Ende des achtzehnten Jahrhunderts verwendete Gitarre. Dieses Instrument hatte Saitenpaare, die Chöre genannt wurden, und keine tiefe E-Saite. Der erste Abschnitt sollte lebhaft und energisch gespielt werden.

11 Die mittleren Noten der drei- und vierstimmigen Akkorde sollten so klar sein wie die äußeren. Der vollständige *Barrégriff* im letzten System ist ziemlich schwierig zu greifen. Das G kann ausgelassen und der Griff damit vermieden werden. Im vorletzten Takt sollten die Gs im Baß ein ganzes Viertel lang ausgehalten werden.

12 Alle Baßnoten sollten ausgehalten und so gehört werden. Die rechte Hand ist vollständig mit einem Fingersatz versehen, es lohnt sich jedoch, andere Fingersätze auszuprobieren. Oft nämlich gibt es zahlreiche verschiedene Lösungen zu Fragen des Fingersatzes der rechten Hand.

13 Lasse dich nicht dazu verleiten, das Stück zu schnell zu spielen. *Maestoso* bedeutet "würdevoll" und meint damit ein gemessenes Tempo. Zwischen den Noten sollten keine Pausen hörbar sein. Die mit *sf* bezeichneten Noten müssen einen Akzent erhalten, der jedoch nicht hart sein darf.

14 Aus *Exercices* Op.24. Das maßgebende Wort in der Tempoangabe ist *Moderato*. Wenn der Anfang zu schnell ist werden die Sechzehntel unspielbar. Achte im Anfangsabschnitt darauf, daß während der Pausen kein Ton hörbar ist. In den Arpeggiopassagen sollte die Baßstimme fest angeschlagen werden.

15 In diesem Stück kann es hilfreich sein, sich die Saiten glühendheiß vorzustellen: die Finger der rechten Hand können sie zwar berühren, jedoch nur für kurze Zeit. Die Note wird gespielt wenn der Finger die Saite berührt. Dies wird dazu beitragen, eine flüssige, zusammenhängende Melodie zu erhalten. Wiederum müssen beide Stimmen klar zu unterscheiden sein.

16 Der Galopp war ein schneller, lebhafter Tanz, der im neunzehnten Jahrhundert populär war. Die Sechzehntel sollten nicht schleppend gespielt werden. Wiederholungen können *piano* gespielt werden.

17 Die Stimmung dieses *Pastorales* sollte gelockert sein, mit einer sanft schaukelnden Bewegung. Die Verzierung in Takt 2 sollte

schnell und auf dem Taktschlag gespielt werden. Sei nicht zu besorgt, wenn der Ton nicht unmittelbar anspricht; es ist keineswegs leicht.

18 Die Achtel im Baß sollten, sofort nachdem sie gespielt wurden, mit dem Daumen der rechten Hand abgestoppt werden; sie sind weniger wirkungsvoll wenn man sie weiterklingen läßt. Die zwei Taktschläge pro Takt sollten genau eingehalten werden.

19 Der Spanier Santiago de Murcia veröffentlichte sein *Resumen de Acompañar*, dem dieses *Menuet* entnommen ist, für die fünfchörige Gitarre. Wie im größten Teil barocker Gitarrenmusik treten auch hier Ornamente auf. Es könnte am besten sein, sie zuerst auszulassen und erst dann hinzuzufügen, wenn das Stück flüssig gespielt werden kann. Die Ornamentierung sollte weder die Anmut noch den Rhythmus der Melodie beeinflussen.

20 Der Daumen sollte über die ersten beiden Noten des Baßmotivs gleiten; die Begleitung muß durchweg zurückhaltend gespielt werden.

21 Alle Obertöne (d.h. die Noten mit rautenförmigem Kopf) sind natürlich und werden gespielt, indem man die Saiten leicht an der Duodezime oder, im Falle des hohen D, am siebten Bund berührt. Wähle das Tempo so, daß du die Obertöne leicht spielen kannst.

22 Aus *Le Second Livre* von 1553 (22 Verso). Über den Lauten- und Gitarrenspieler Guillaume Morley, der im sechzehnten Jahrhundert lebte, ist sehr wenig bekannt, auch nicht Geburts- oder Todesdatum. Die Kompositionen für die vierchörige Gitarre, die hier von der Originaltabulatur transkribiert sind, sind die frühesten Stücke dieser Sammlung. Das vierchörige Instrument hatte vier Saitenpaare, die nach D G B E gestimmt waren, wie die vier obersten Saiten der modernen Gitarre. Diese *Gaillarde* (oder *Galliard*), ein damals populärer Tanz, sollte mit lebhaftem und pointiertem Rhythmus gespielt werden.

23 Aus *Le Second Livre* von 1553 (24 Verso). Während die *Gaillarde* (Nr. 22) aus Italien stammt, war der *Bransle* (oder *Branle*) ursprünglich ein ländlicher französischer Tanz. Unter dem Namen *Brawl* war er auch in England beliebt. Die Sechzehntel sollten sehr langsam und mit sorgfältiger Beachtung des Fingersatzes für die rechte Hand geübt werden.

24 Robert de Visées *Gavotte* wurde einem Manuskript in der Bibliothèque Nationale in Paris (Res. F. 844, S. 200) entnommen und datiert etwa vom Ende des siebzehnten Jahrhunderts. Wie im Stück von Santiago de Murcia finden sich auch hier viele Verzierungen, und wiederum könnte es nützlich sein, sie anfangs auszulassen, um einen gleichmäßigen Rhythmus zu entwickeln. Äußerst wirkungsvoll ist es, die Saiten mit dem Zeigefinger von oben nach unten zu schlagen.

25 Spiele dieses Stück mit gleichmäßigem, wiegendem Rhythmus, wie ein Schlaflied. Die Pausen sollten genau eingehalten, keine jedoch zwischen den Akkorden hinzugefügt werden! Die letzten vier Takte können sehr leise und allmählich verklingend gespielt werden.

26 Aus *Collecion 10ª. de Ejercicios* (Nr. 9). Jose Ferrer, der aus Barcelona stammte, schrieb eine große Anzahl von Studien und Etüden, von denen die meisten jedoch anscheinend niemals veröffentlicht wurden. Dieser *Vals* beschwört, wie so viele seiner Kompositionen, eine sehr spanische Atmosphäre. In der fallenden Passage der Takte 5-7 kann die oberste Note jeder Gruppe bis zum Beginn des folgenden Taktes ausgehalten werden. Die Baßnoten im zweiten Abschnitt sollten kräftig, mit einem *Apoyando*-Anschlag gespielt werden.

27 Aus *Resumen de Acompañar* von 1714 (S. 84). Spiele dies in schlichtem Stil, so daß die Klarheit beider Stimmen gewährleistet ist. Die Triller in der Musik dieser Periode beginnen im allgemeinen einen Ton über der geschriebenen Note; dies ist hier durch Vorschläge angezeigt.

28 Aus *Collecion 12ª. de Ejercicios* (Nr. 2). Dieses lebhafte Stück sollte mit Charme und Humor gespielt werden, wobei darauf zu achten ist, daß die Akkorde im dritten Takt klar und im Takt gespielt werden. Die Ornamente klingen am wirkungsvollsten, wenn sie schnell und nachdrücklich auf dem Taktschlag gespielt werden.

29 Aus *Le Premier Livre* von 1552 (23 Verso). Die Läufe in *Buffons* (Clowns) sollten langsam und mit einem Minimum an Fingerbewegung in beiden Händen geübt werden; dann spiele sie allmählich schneller. Wenn gut gespielt, ist das Stück ein beeindruckendes und glänzendes Konzertstück.

30 & 31 Dieses beiden Stücke hat der englische Komponist Nicholas Maw eigens für diese Sammlung geschrieben. In Nr. 30 mag die Taktangabe von $\frac{5}{4}$ zunächst etwas seltsam erscheinen; sie findet sich jedoch oft in modernen Kompositionen und dürfte, wenn man genau zählt, keinerlei Schwierigkeiten bereiten. Die Daumenarpeggios sollten nicht zu aggressiv gespielt werden. Um sie langsamer zu spielen, wird mit dem Daumen diagonal nach unten geschlagen; man beginnt dazu mit der E-Baßsaite am Mittelloch und bewegt sich für die oberen Saiten auf den Steg zu. In Nr. 31 wurden die offenen Baßsaiten vom Komponisten geschickt für eine interessante rhythmische Begleitung verwendet. Diese sollte nicht schwerfällig klingen, noch die Melodie stören.

32 & 33 Guillermo Flores Méndez ist ein zeitgenössischer mexikanischer Komponist, der viel Gitarrenmusik geschrieben hat. *Obsesión* spielt man am besten in sehr langsamem und gemessenem Tempo; beachte die Metronomangabe des Komponisten. Dasselbe Tempo muß für den synkopierten Mittelabschnitt eingehalten, und Dis und E durchweg klar und gleichmäßig gespielt werden. Nr. 33, aus *Cuatro Miniaturas*, ist im Grunde ein ungezwungener Walzer.

34-37 Stanley Glasser hat in diese Suite verschiedene musikalische Elemente aus Afrika einbezogen. In den letzten zwei Takten von *Striding* kann die Seite des Daumens dazu benützt werden, auf den Steg zu klopfen. Dieser Effekt ist als *Tamburo* bekannt. Im letzten Takt sollte der zweite Finger mit ziemlich rascher Bewegung und ohne vom Griffbrett weggehoben zu werden den Hals hinauf zum A gleiten. Beachte, daß in *Mlengana Rock* die Kommas (d.h. kurze Fermaten, nicht so lang wie ⌒) zwischen die musikalischen Aussagen gesetzt sind, so daß dadurch der Satz weitaus weniger schwierig zu spielen ist. Beachte auch die abrupten dynamischen Wechsel, vor allem am Ende. Diese Stücke sind hinsichtlich ihrer Klangwelt recht verschieden von den übrigen der Sammlung. Jede musikalische Phrase sollte als ein eigenes kleines Stück behandelt werden; dies wird dazu beitragen, die Komposition als Ganzes würdigen zu können.

Pig in a Rain Puddle will auf musikalische Weise ein Schwein darstellen, das darum kämpft, sich zu befreien. Die Kästchen und Pfeile mögen zunächst sehr seltsam erscheinen; ihr Zweck ist es, dem Spieler die Möglichkeit zu geben, darüber zu entscheiden, wie das Stück am Ende klingt: beginne bei ☐1 und folge den Pfeilen; wiederhole es in einer verschiedenen Reihenfolge, aber ende mit ☐5 . Das Zufallselement, das durch die Wahl des Spielers einbezogen wird, ist als *Aleatorik* bekannt. Das Hinuntergleiten (Glissando) in Kästchen ☐3 ist das gleiche wie in *Striding*. Die Zeichen ↓ und ♯ bedeuten: spiele einen Viertel- bzw. einen Dreivierteltön höher (indem du die Saite spannst).

Die Akzente in *Donkey Ride* sind ziemlich wichtig; das Zeichen > verlangt einen härteren Anschlag als das Zeichen − , unter dem eher ein nachdrücklicher Akzent zu verstehen ist. Im Stück ist ein Eselsschrei verborgen.